The Black Crowes
$hake Your Money Maker

As recorded by THE BLACK CROWES on DEF AMERICAN Records

Management: Angelus Entertainment - Pete Angelus/Patrick Whitley
Transcribed by Brad McPhail
Edited by Steve Gorenberg, Kerry O'Brien and Jeff Jacobson
Music Engraving by W.R. Music
Copy Editor: Cathy Cassinos-Carr
Production Manager: Daniel Rosenbaum
Art Direction: Kerstin Fairbend
Administration: Monica Corton
Director of Music: Mark Phillips

ISBN: 0-89524-655-4

The Black Crowes

From the South with plenty of high flyin' attitude swoop the Crowes! Their butt-shaking, hip-dipping, blusey rock 'n' roll on *Shake Your Moneymaker* (Def American) could peel the paint off any ol' thing in your music room.

These five dudes from Atlanta play the kind of stuff your older brother probably bragged about when Rod "the bod" Stewart beat up the airwaves with Faces way back when. Their slash-and-trash bursts from the guitar duo of Rich Robinson and Jeff Cease would even put pie-eatin' grins on Messrs. Richards' and Wood's faces. Of course, you've already figured that out. Yer just lookin' to cop some of their nifty riffs. Well, before you do, let me tell you a little more about these good ol' boys:

NEIL ZLOZOWER

Chris Robinson.....vocals
Rich Robinson.....guitars
Jeff Cease.....guitars
Johnny Colt.....bass
Steve Gorman.....drums & cymbals

The brothers Robinson had this band called Mr. Crowe's Garden about five years ago. Chris was just 18; Rich, 15. They played their first gig in Chattanooga, Tenn. for $50. Hardly an awesome debut considering that the check bounced, but nonetheless it was a start.

Well, about two years after that they added drummer man Steve Gorman, who had kind of a steadying influence on the band, and after trying six bass players they finally landed groove master Johnny Colt. It wasn't until 1988, though, that they decided to add a second guitarist, Jeff Cease, who turned out to be the perfect complement to Rich. As Rich puts it, "Jeff had the right attitude from the start. He came in to enhance what I was playin'; to play solos, really cool solos. That way I could play the songs as a whole instead of just bits and pieces." With a lineup that now felt right, the Crowes hit the road with flash and fury. It wasn't long before Def American Records came knocking on their door and readied them for this debut.

Besides the smokin' singles "Jealous Again" and "Hard To Handle," pay attention to the mid-tempo, soulful rocker "Sister Luck," which features guest pianist/organist Chuck Leavell (ex-Allman Brothers). And throughout the LP, some near-flawless chestnuts of string bending keep it movin' in the right direction. You'd swear this was *Exile on Main Street* material, and you don't get any meatier than that. In fact, "Thick N' Thin" rocks just as hard as "Rip This Joint" from that very same Rolling Stone benchmark.

What equipment do they use to get such a great sound? Says younger brother Rich, "I'm playing only a Telecaster and Jeff plays either a Les Paul or a Firebird. I play through a straight Marshall, nothing else; no effects or anything. In the studio I used a Fender Twin Reverb and Showman amps." Forget the gadgets, just plenty of sweat and—his secret weapon—various tunings. "People come up to me and say, 'I tried to play "Jealous Again" and I just can't do it!' And I say, 'Oh, maybe you're in the wrong tuning.' I use tons of different tunings." Far be it from me to ask him which ones; I'll leave the detective work up to you guitar mavericks.

But do the Crowes have soul? Sure as yer reading this, they do. If you want R&B fury, check out the Otis Redding classic "Hard To Handle," redone Crowes style. It chugs and it slugs and punches along, fueled by drummer Gorman and bassist Colt. Ohhh, baby! Brother Otis must be doin' the boogaloo in heaven every time he hears this electrifying version. The wailing guitar solos by Jeff and Rich would do legendary guitar maestro Steve Cropper (of Booker T & The M.G.s fame) proud. And "Seeing Things," a mournful soul ballad, offers plenty of fire to fuel even the staunchest R&B purist. Leavell punches up his Hammond Organ and his piano to keep you reelin' all the way out, and with soul sister Laura Creamer providing gospel-tinged background vocal support on the chorus ("I'm seeing things for the first time … "), I'm seein' nothin' but the best music to come from the South since the aforementioned Allman Brothers. Yeah, it's a mighty big claim, but these dudes back it all up.

Which tune best sums up the Crowes' attitude? "The album as a whole has the attitude, but the one that explains it best is 'Stare It Cold,' " says Rich. "All my influences are there: Mississippi Fred McDowell, Muddy Waters, Ron Woods (when he was in Faces), Keith Richards, Malcolm Young, Jimmy Page." (Did he forget anyone?)

And one other thing, Brother Rich: What choo wanna tell the kids out there who're thinkin' about growin' up to be rock 'n' rollers? "Well, to be honest, I never really learned how to read music, but I learned how to rock 'n' roll. I think this book can help you, if you let it. And most importantly, write your own songs. Do what you do and don't ever compromise!"

—Mark J. Petracca

CONTENTS

FULL COLOR FOLD-OUT FOLLOWS PAGE 16

 **CHERRY LANE MUSIC: THE PRINT COMPANY**

EXECUTIVE: Michael Lefferts, President; Kathleen A. Maloney, Director of Advertising and Promotion; Rock Stamberg, Assistant Director of Advertising and Promotion; Len Handler, Creative Services Manager; Monica Corton, Contracts Administrator; Karen Carey, Division Secretary; Karen DeCrenza, Executive Secretary.
MUSIC: Mark Phillips, Director of Music; Jon Chappell, Associate Director of Music; Gordon Hallberg, Computer Music Engraver; Steve Gorenberg, Music Editor; Kerry O'Brien, Music Editor; Cathy Cassinos-Carr, Copy Editor.
ART: Kerstin A. Fairbend, Art Director; Michele A. Lyons, Assistant Art Director; Rosemary Cappa, Art Assistant.
PRODUCTION: Daniel Rosenbaum, Production Manager; James Piacentino, Production Coordinator.

TWICE AS HARD

Words and Music by
Richard Robinson and Christopher Robinson

as it was the first time_ I said good - bye._

And no one 'll ev - er wan - na know. Love ain't fun - ny. A crime in the wink of an eye._

Guitar solo

*standard tuning

JEALOUS AGAIN

Words and Music by
Richard Robinson and Christopher Robinson

1. Cheat the odds that made you, brave to try to gam-ble that time.____

2.3. *See additional lyrics*

*Strike chord on beat 1, 3rd time only.

Well, I'm feel-in' dirt-y laun-dry, send-ing sick-ness on down the line.____

Tell you what, 'cause I'm jeal-ous,____

Rhy. Fill 2 (Gtr. I)

Rhy. Fill 4 (Gtr. II)

*Doubled by acous. gtr.

Additional Lyrics

2. Always drunk on Sunday, tryin' to feel like I'm at home.
   Smell the gasoline burnin', boys out feelin' nervous and cold. Oh yeah. *(To Chorus)*

3. Never felt like smilin', sugar gonna kill me yet.
   Found me loose-lipped and laughin', singin' songs, ain't got no regret. *(To Chorus)*

SISTER LUCK

Words and Music by
Richard Robinson and Christopher Robinson

Chorus

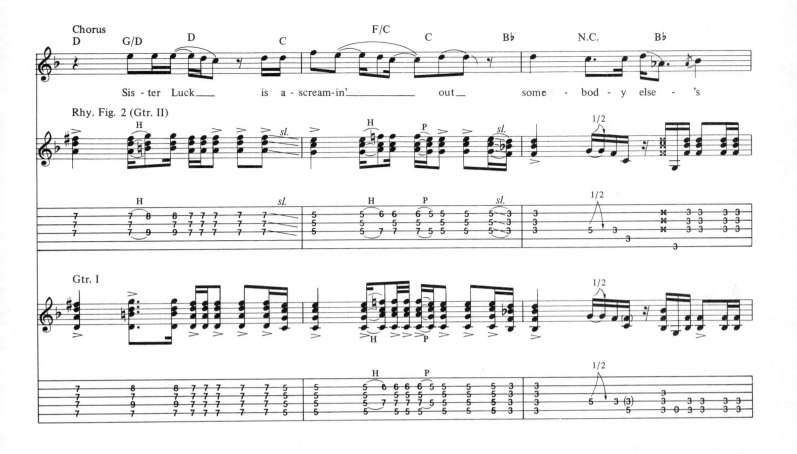

Sis - ter Luck___ is a - scream-in'___ out___ some - bod - y else - 's

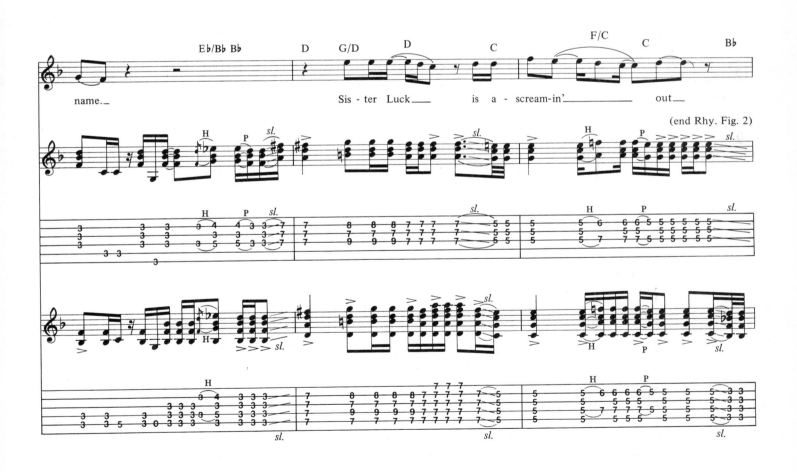

name.___   Sis - ter Luck___ is a - scream-in'___ out___

(end Rhy. Fig. 2)

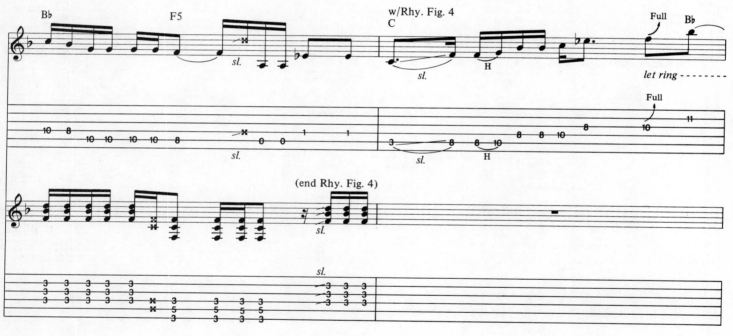

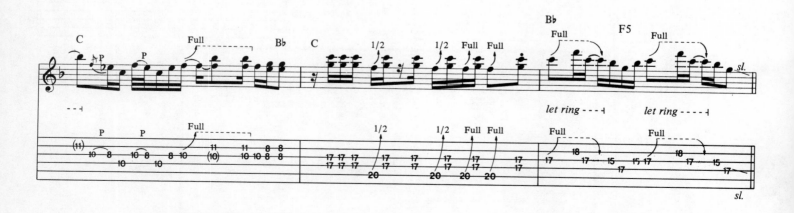

COULD I'VE BEEN SO BLIND

Words and Music by
Richard Robinson and Christopher Robinson

*Use open E tuning (low to high): E B E G# B E

Oh, ___ could I've been ___ so blind? ___ So emp-ty that I've

___ nev-er felt warm. ___ Can I spell ___ it out? ___ Turn ___ my-self

___ out of my home. ___ Look-in' like ___ a fool, ___ feel-in' e-

could I _____ ev - er have been _____ so blind?

Could I _____ ev - er have been _____ so blind? Yeah, ___

could I _____ ev - er have been _____ so blind?

Additional Lyrics

3. Hardest thing that I ever had to do
   Was stand up straight and tell it all to you.
   Look you right in the eye,
   Tell you baby, sorry but I had lied.
3rd Pre-chorus: And now it looks like innocence is gone.
   I know right and I know what's wrong.
   Feelin' lonely, that's the way it goes sometimes. *(To Coda)*

SEEING THINGS

Words and Music by
Richard Robinson and Christopher Robinson

*Use open G tuning (low to high): D G D G B D and place capo at 2nd fret.
TAB numbers shown are actual fret numbers. A "2" in TAB is thought
of as an open string.

*Standard tuning

1st, 2nd Verses
w/Rhy. Fig. 1 (2 times)

1. I find it hard to shed a tear.
2. See additional lyrics

Brought it on your-self, my dear.

Riff B

And wrong, yes, I may be.

Don't leave a light on for me

A/G

1.

'cause I ain't com-in' home.

It hurts me, ba-by, to be a-lone.

Rhy. Fig. 2

(end Riff B)

Yes,__ it hurts me, ba - by.__

And this love__ tears__ us__ a - part.__ Won't find me bent down__ on__ my

knees.__ Oh__ yeah.__ Ain't__ bend - in' o - ver back - wards, ba — by, not to

Additional Lyrics

2. A hundred years will never ease.
Hearin' things I won't believe.
I saw it with my own two eyes.
All the pain I can't hide.
And this pain starts in my heart.
And this love tears us apart. *(To Pre-chorus)*

HARD TO HANDLE

Words and Music by
Otis Redding, Alvertis Isbell
and Allen Jones

I've got some good old lovin' and I got some more in store. _____ Uh,

when I get through throwin' it on ya, you got to come back for more. _____

(end Rhy. Fig. 1)

Chorus
F#5

Boys have things that come by the doz-en. That ain't noth-in' but drug-store lov-in'.

Pret-ty lit-tle thing, let me light your can-dle 'cause, uh, ma-ma, I'm sure hard to han-dle now, yes, a-round.

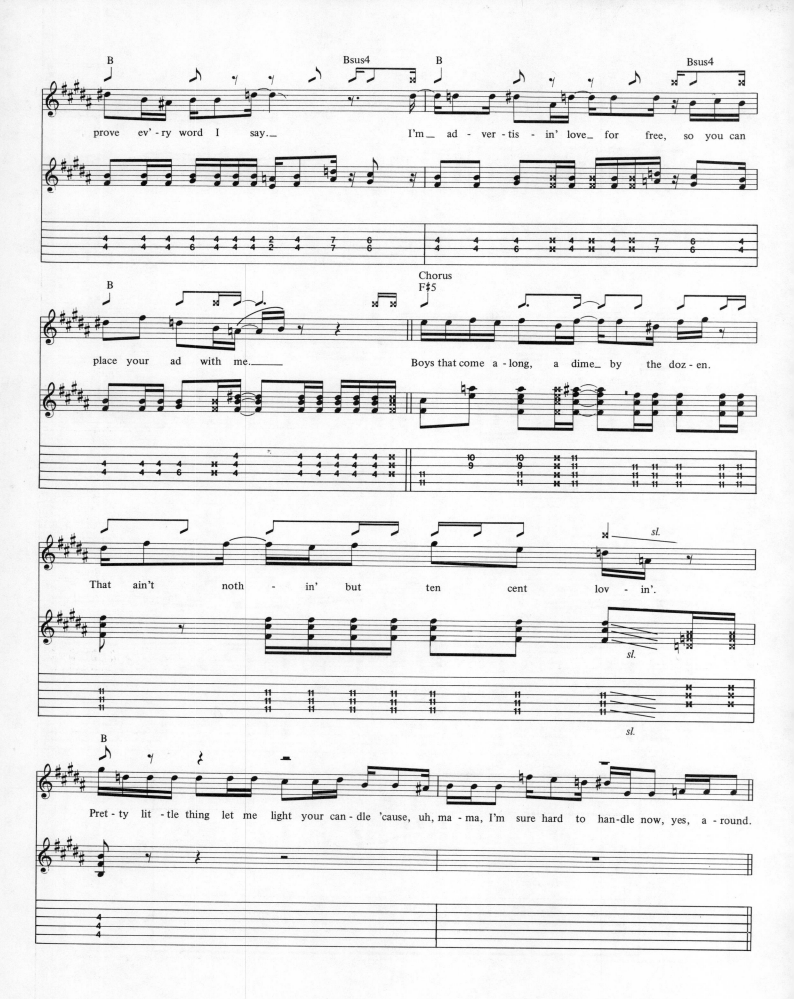

THICK N' THIN

Words and Music by
Richard Robinson and Christopher Robinson

let it go,— let it loose— on to the wind.— Well, it's thick.—

Thick n' thin.— Oh,— God!—Let it loose.

*straight 8ths

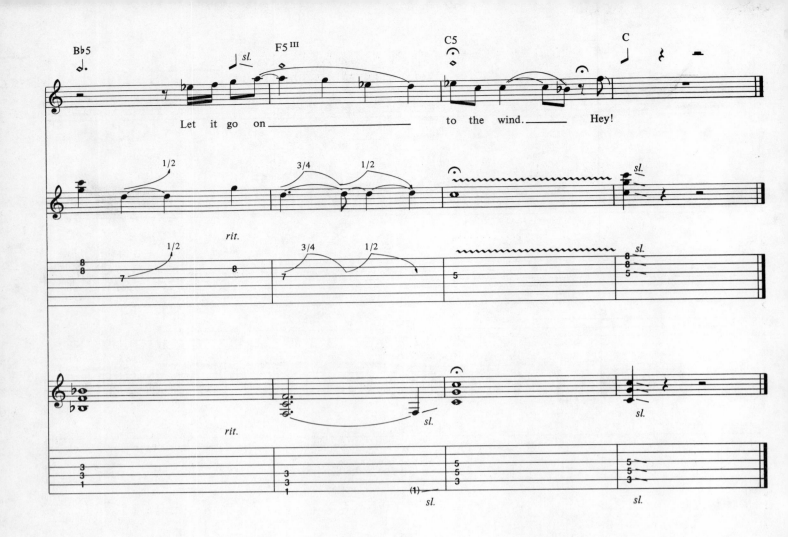

Let it go on _____ to the wind. _____ Hey!

Additional Lyrics

2. Heard a clock tock tickin'.
   I see the madam start bitchin'.
   I see the boys, they itch itchin'.
   The girls don't ever know what they're missin'.

2nd Pre-chorus: But it sounds like shit to me.
   Last laugh mine will be, yeah.
   I don't believe she's clean. *(To Chorus)*

SHE TALKS TO ANGELS

Words and Music by
Richard Robinson and Christopher Robinson

*Use open E tuning (low to high): E B E G#B E

She nev-er men-tions the word ad -

1st Verse
w/Rhy. Fig. 2 (3 times)

dic - tion ___   in   cer -tain com -   pa - ny. ___

Yes,   she'll tell you she's   an or - phan ___   af - ter   you meet her fam -

i - ly. ___

Rhy. Fill 1

(end Rhy. Fill 1)

2. She paints her eyes as black as

Rhy. Fig. 3

*Harm.

(end Rhy. Fig. 3)

*Harm.

*Harm. refers to all
notes except low E (⑥open)

Additional Lyrics

3. She keeps a lock of hair in her pocket.
She wears a cross around her neck.
The hair is from a little boy,
And the cross from someone she has not met, well, not yet. *(To Chorus)*

4. *Repeat 2nd Verse*

STRUTTIN' BLUES

Words and Music by
Richard Robinson and Christopher Robinson

STARE IT COLD

Words and Music by
Richard Robinson and Christopher Robinson

1.4. Under the weather, I never got better, wrapped up in my disease._____ Mile_____ away, she wanna

Additional Lyrics

3. Never thought about it and never no question.
   Seein' where I'd gone wrong.
   No kiss made it magic if that old girl has had it.
   Then it's time for me to run along. *(To Chorus)*

TABLATURE EXPLANATION

TABLATURE: A six-line staff that graphically represents the guitar fingerboard, with the top line indicating the highest sounding string (high E). By placing a number on the appropriate line, the string and fret of any note can be indicated. The number 0 represents an open string. For example:

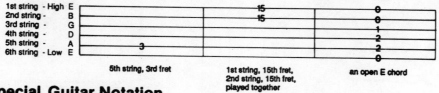

1st string - High E
2nd string - B
3rd string - G
4th string - D
5th string - A
6th string - Low E

5th string, 3rd fret   1st string, 15th fret, 2nd string, 15th fret, played together   an open E chord

Definitions for Special Guitar Notation

BEND: Strike the note and bend up ½ step (one fret).

BEND: Strike the note and bend up a whole step (two frets).

BEND AND RELEASE: Strike the note and bend up ½ (or whole) step, then release the bend back to the original note. All three notes are tied, only the first note is struck.

PRE-BEND: Bend the note up ½ (or whole) step, then strike it.

PRE-BEND AND RELEASE: Bend the note up ½ (or whole) step. Strike it and release the bend back to the original note.

UNISON BEND: Strike the two notes simultaneously and bend the lower note up to the pitch of the higher.

VIBRATO: The string is vibrated by rapidly bending and releasing the note with the left hand or tremolo bar.

WIDE OR EXAGGERATED VIBRATO: The pitch is varied to a greater degree by vibrating with the left hand or tremolo bar.

SLIDE: Strike the first note and then slide the same left-hand finger up or down to the second note. The second note is not struck.

SLIDE: Same as above, except the second note is struck.

SLIDE: Slide up to the note indicated from a few frets below.

SLIDE: Strike the note and slide up or down an indefinite number of frets, releasing finger pressure at the end of the slide.

HAMMER-ON: Strike the first (low) note, then sound the higher note with another finger by fretting it without picking.

HAMMER-ON: Without picking, sound the note indicated by sharply fretting the note with a left-hand finger.

PULL-OFF: Place both fingers on the notes to be sounded. Strike the first note and without picking, pull the finger off to sound the second (lower) note.

TRILL: Very rapidly alternate between the note indicated and the small note shown is parentheses by hammering on and pulling off.

TAPPING: Hammer ("tap") the fret indicated with the right-hand index or middle finger and pull off to the note fretted by the left hand.

PICK SLIDE: The edge of the pick is rubbed down the length of the string producing a scratchy sound.

TREMOLO PICKING: The note is picked as rapidly and continuously as possible.

RAKE: Drag the pick across the strings indicated from low to high with a single downward motion.

ARPEGGIO: Play the notes of the chord indicated by quickly rolling them from bottom to top.

NATURAL HARMONIC: Strike the note while the left hand lightly touches the string over the fret indicated.

ARTIFICIAL HARMONIC: The note is fretted normally and a harmonic is produced by adding the edge of the thumb or the tip of the index finger of the right hand to the normal pick attack. High volume or distortion will allow for a greater variety of harmonics.

TREMOLO BAR: The pitch of the note or chord is dropped a specified number of steps then returned to the original pitch.

PALM MUTING: The note is partially muted by the right hand lightly touching the string(s) just before the bridge.

MUFFLED STRINGS: A percussive sound is produced by laying the left hand across the strings without depressing them and striking them with the right hand.

RHYTHM SLASHES: Strum chords in rhythm indicated. Use chord voicings found in the fingering diagrams at the top of the first page of the transcription.

RHYTHM SLASHES (SINGLE NOTES): Single notes can be indicated in rhythm slashes. The circled number above the note name indicates which string to play. When successive notes are played on the same string, only the fret numbers are given.

NOTE: Tablature numbers in parentheses mean:

1. The note is being sustained over a barline (note in standard notation is tied), or

2. The note is sustained, but a new articulation (such as a hammer-on, pull-off, slide or vibrato) begins, or

3. The note is a barely audible "ghost" note (note in standard notation is also in parentheses).

Definitions of Musical Symbols

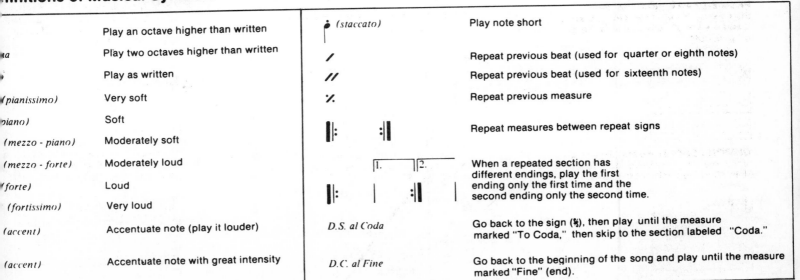

	Play an octave higher than written	(staccato)	Play note short
8va	Play two octaves higher than written	/	Repeat previous beat (used for quarter or eighth notes)
	Play as written	//	Repeat previous beat (used for sixteenth notes)
(pianissimo)	Very soft	%	Repeat previous measure
(piano)	Soft	‖: :‖	Repeat measures between repeat signs
(mezzo - piano)	Moderately soft		
(mezzo - forte)	Moderately loud	1. 2.	When a repeated section has different endings, play the first ending only the first time and the second ending only the second time.
(forte)	Loud	‖: :‖	
(fortissimo)	Very loud		
(accent)	Accentuate note (play it louder)	D.S. al Coda	Go back to the sign (%), then play until the measure marked "To Coda," then skip to the section labeled "Coda."
(accent)	Accentuate note with great intensity	D.C. al Fine	Go back to the beginning of the song and play until the measure marked "Fine" (end).

SPEND A YEAR WITH

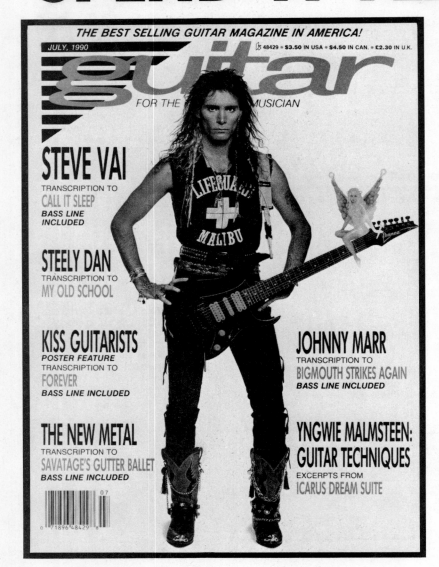

THE BEST SELLING GUITAR MAGAZINE IN AMERICA!

JULY, 1990

guitar
FOR THE ... MUSICIAN

JS 48429 • $3.50 IN USA • $4.50 IN CAN. • £2.30 IN U.K.

STEVE VAI
TRANSCRIPTION TO
CALL IT SLEEP
BASS LINE INCLUDED

STEELY DAN
TRANSCRIPTION TO
MY OLD SCHOOL

KISS GUITARISTS
POSTER FEATURE
TRANSCRIPTION TO
FOREVER
BASS LINE INCLUDED

THE NEW METAL
TRANSCRIPTION TO
SAVATAGE'S GUTTER BALLET
BASS LINE INCLUDED

JOHNNY MARR
TRANSCRIPTION TO
BIGMOUTH STRIKES AGAIN
BASS LINE INCLUDED

**YNGWIE MALMSTEEN:
GUITAR TECHNIQUES**
EXCERPTS FROM
ICARUS DREAM SUITE

0 71896 48429 6   07

Eddie Van Halen
Steve Vai
Randy Rhoads
Yngwie Malmsteen
Jimi Hendrix
Vinnie Moore
Stevie Ray Vaughan
Guns N' Roses
Jeff Watson
Carlos Santana
Neal Schon
Eric Clapton
Jimmy Page
Jake E. Lee
Brad Gillis
George Lynch
Metallica
Keith Richards
Jeff Beck
Michael Schenker ...

AND SAVE $14.00 off the newsstand price!

Just $27.95 buys you a year's subscription to GUITAR and the chance to spend 12 months studying the techniques and the artistry of the world's best guitar performers.

Get started ... mail the coupon below!

Every issue of GUITAR gives you:

• sheet music you can't get anywhere else—with accur... transcriptions of the original artists.

• in-depth interviews with guitar greats who candidly disc... the nuts and bolts of what they do.

• columns and articles on the music, the equipment and ... techniques that are making waves.

Become a better guitarist and performer. Study with the profession als every month in GUITAR FOR THE PRACTICING MUSICIAN.

To start your subscription — *and save 33% off the cover price* — w...
GUITAR P.O. Box 53063, Boulder, CO 80322-3063